A Children's Treasury of
Rebbe Nachman's Tales

The Merchant of Breslov

Adapted by
C. Levin and M. Mykoff

Illustrated by
Aharon Friedman

Dedicated to the advancement of children's education
in honor of our children

Jack, Michael, Steven, Daniel and Grace

by

Joe and Trina Cayre

Book Design: Ben Gasner

All rights reserved
©Breslov Research Institute 1997
ISBN 0-930213-70-X

Published by
Breslov Research Institute
Jerusalem/New York
POB 5370, Jerusalem, Israel
POB 587, Monsey, NY 10952-0587

Printed in Israel

Dear Parents

Rebbe Nachman's stories and tales have delighted the young and the young at heart ever since he first told them nearly 200 years ago. But as anyone who has read or heard these stories knows, the Rebbe's purpose in storytelling was not so much to entertain as to educate and inspire. Bearing this in mind, we have added a "Things to Think About" page at the end of the story. Whether your children have read the story on their own or whether you've read it to them, we're sure you'll find "Things to Think About" a helpful guide for exploring with them the valuable concepts expressed within the story's framework. You may also have some of your own insights to share with the children. Go right ahead. Rebbe Nachman's tales are multifaceted, lending themselves to many levels of interpretation.

In the town of Breslov, there once lived a wealthy storekeeper. His name was Moshe Merchant.

Moshe sold many, many interesting things in his shop. His shelves and barrels were always filled with exactly what people wanted to buy.

One day a band of robbers came and broke into Moshe's shop. They stole most of Moshe's money and almost all the things he had to sell.

Moshe was very sad, but he did not give up. He collected whatever the robbers had left, bought some more interesting things to sell, and again opened his shop for business.

A few months later the robbers returned. This time they took just about everything Moshe had in his shop.

Still Moshe did not give up. He again collected the few things the robbers had not stolen. His wife gave him her jewelry as well, which Moshe traded for more things to sell. Once again Moshe managed to open up his shop for business.

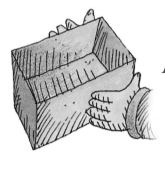 Although Moshe Merchant was no longer rich, the shop did earn him enough money to buy food and clothing for his family. But then the robbers came again. This time they took everything. Now Moshe had nothing left.

This time again, Moshe did not give up. He went around the town of Breslov asking his friends to help him. With the little bit of money he collected Moshe bought a few small objects, like pots and pans and other things which are made in towns.

Then Moshe went traveling around the countryside from one village to another, where he traded his pots and pans to the village people for chickens and eggs. He then took the chickens and eggs back to Breslov, where he sold them for a small profit. This was how Moshe tried to earn a living.

One day Moshe was on his way to one of the villages carrying a few things to sell and a bit of food. Suddenly a robber rode up to him on a big horse, carrying two huge bundles. When the robber saw Moshe, he wanted to steal the little bundle Moshe was carrying.

Moshe started crying. "Please don't take it," he begged. "This is all I have left in the world!"

But the robber did not care, and he grabbed Moshe's little bundle.

Moshe cried and felt very bitter. "So many bad things have happened to me! First the robbers took all my money and all the things from my shop. Now even the little bit I managed to buy again has been stolen from me."

Just then Moshe noticed that the robber had fallen off his horse. He tried to stand up, but the horse kept knocking him down with its big hooves. Finally, the robber fell down and did not get up.

Moshe ran over to look and he saw that the robber was dead. Then Moshe opened up the robber's huge bundles.

What a surprise! Inside the bundles he found his money and all the things which had been stolen from him in the past.

Moshe Merchant was delighted to get back all his things and he hurried back to Breslov to tell his family the good news. Then he again opened his shop, and became a wealthy storekeeper once more.

EPILOGUE

Rebbe Nachman teaches us an important lesson with this story. Many times we try to do the right thing, only to find that problems get in our way. We should never give up! Even if much of what we have already done is taken from us, we have to look for the little bit of good we have left. We have to keep on believing in God's goodness and kindness, and with all our hearts we must ask God to help us. In the end, not only will our troubles go away, but we will get back everything we had before.

THINGS TO THINK ABOUT

1. What was so very special about Moshe Merchant?
   a. He was rich.
   b. He worked hard.
   c. He never gave up.

2. Even after being robbed three times, Moshe did not give up. He reopened his shop again and again. Did it ever happen to you that you tried to do something, but just could not manage? How did you react? Did you keep on trying?

3. Rebbe Nachman tells us that a person can find the strength to start over again by making use of even a little bit of something good. Where in the story do we see that Moshe Merchant knew this?

4. What does this story teach us about the robber? Do you think someone who steals from others always gets to enjoy what he steals?

5. Sometimes we work hard to reach a goal and are just about to succeed, when suddenly something goes wrong. It may then seem that we are back to where we were when we started, and that we have lost everything. The truth is, the good things we have already done are very much like Moshe Merchant's shop and everything he owned. Can you figure out how?

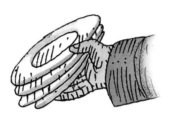